Play Time

Note on the Revised Edition

HAPPY VENTURE was conceived and has been validated as a basic teaching method, and as such has proved outstandingly successful. Our language is a living one, however, and so certain expressions appearing in the original edition have now gone out of use.

Before his death in 1969, Professor Schonell was actively engaged in discussion with the publishers about the revision of the entire series. Unfortunately he was not able to undertake this before he died.

After consultations with practising teachers throughout the country and abroad, it became apparent to the publishers that the principles on which the series was based had not altered, but that minor changes to up-date the text could be made without affecting the well-tested structure of the series.

Accordingly, in this book, teachers will find:

'a' and 'g' replaced by script 'ɑ' and 'g'; new illustrations throughout; textual alteration on p. 25.

The publishers acknowledge the help and advice of Miss Angela Ridsdale of Toorak Teachers' College, Malvern, Victoria, Australia, in the revision of this series.

OLIVER AND BOYD
Robert Stevenson House
1-3 Baxter's Place, Leith Walk
Edinburgh EH1 3BB
A Division of Longman Group Ltd

First Published 1939
Second Edition 1958
Revised Edition 1971
Ninth impression 1982
ISBN 0 05 002379 9

Printed in Hong Kong by
Commonwealth Printing Press Ltd

Happy Venture
Book One

Play Time

FRED J. SCHONELL
and IRENE SERJEANT

Illustrated by Will Nickless

OLIVER AND BOYD : EDINBURGH

Fluff is a big cat.
She has a big basket.

Dick will bring the basket
for Fluff.

It is by the tree.

Fluff runs to the basket
and sits in it.

Here is a little kitten.
It is Fluff's kitten.

The little kitten can run
and play.

She has a ball.
She will play with Fluff
and the dog.

The little cat can run.
Run, little kitten, run.

The little cat will not stop.
Stop, little kitten, stop.

See this little cat stop.

It is fun for her to play.

Nip runs to see the kitten.
He will play with her.

The kitten runs, and Nip
runs on and on and on.

Stop, Nip, stop.
He will not stop.
He is a bad dog.

The dog will not stop.
The kitten will not stop.

Dora runs to Nip.
Nip will run and play.

You bad dog, Nip.
You did not stop.

Dora did not take Nip
with her.

The kitten is so little,
she can sit in Dick's shoe.

The shoe is wet
with the mud.

We will get the kitten
and take her to Fluff
in her basket.

7

The little kitten runs
    to the wet mud
    and sits in it.

Fluff can see her kitten.
" You can not sit in the mud,
    you bad little cat," she said.

The bad little cat said,
    " I will sit in the mud.
    I am a big cat."

The bad little kitten sits
in the mud.

Her mummy said,
" You will get wet."

" I am wet with mud,"
said the kitten.

Fluff said, " I will wash you.
I will wash off the mud."

"We will play,"
   said Dick and Dora.

Dick runs and Dora hops.
Dora hops on a line.

"This is my line," said Dora.
   "See, Dick, I am on my line.
   I can hop on my line,"
   said Dora.

"It is fun to get on a line
   and hop."

Dick said, "I will not run.
I will hop.
I will hop to you, Dora.
We will hop, hop, hop."
Dora hops to Fluff's basket.

Here is Dick with Dora.

Dick said to Dora,
  " We will run to the tree."

Dora said, " You can run
  with me."

One, two, and off run Dick
and Dora.

Dick fell. He did not get
  to the tree.

Jack said, " See me jump.
  I can do big jumps.
  I can run and I can jump."

Dick said, " I will hop
  and you can jump
  to the line."

So Dick hops
  and Jack jumps
  to the line.

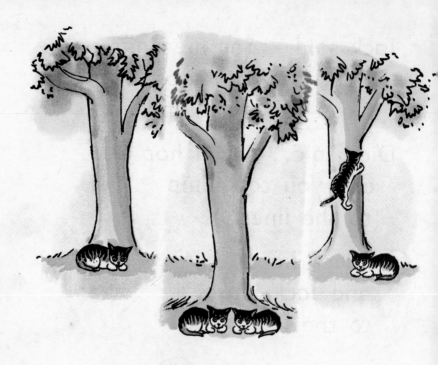

One little kitten sits
by the tree.

Two little kittens sit
by the tree.

One little kitten runs
up the tree.

So one little kitten sits
by the tree.

Jack and Dick play
with a little ball.

Dick's shoe is off.

" The dog will take
my shoe," said Dick,
" so I will hop to it."

He can not get it.

" Stop, Nip, stop," said Dick.

He is a bad dog.
He will not stop.

" I can get the shoe for you.
I can run," said Jack.

Jack runs and Dick hops.

Jack will bring the shoe
for Dick.

Jack will get his ball.

"I am to play bat and ball
with Dick," said Jack.

Dick will get his big bat.

Dick and Jack run
to the big tree to play.

Dick has the bat.
Jack has the ball.

"I will throw my ball,"
said Jack.

"I will hit it," said Dick.

16

Nip will run
  to get the ball.

He will bring it to Jack.

Jack said,
  " I will throw the ball.
  You can hit it."

Dick did not hit the ball
  with his bat.

The ball hit the tree.

17

Dick, Jack and Dora play
with a bat and ball.

Dick hits the ball and runs.
Dick has one run.

Dora throws the ball to Jack.

Dick hits the ball and runs.
" Two runs for me," said Dick.

Dora throws the ball to Jack.

Dick hits the ball and runs.
" Three runs for me," said Dick.

Dora can skip.
She can skip well.
One, two, three.
Skip, skip, skip.

May can skip well.
One, two, three.

Dora and May can skip well.
" We can skip well," said May.

Dora will run, run, run.

Dick will hop, hop, hop.

May will skip,
  one, two, three.

Jack will jump,
  one, two, three.

See us run and skip.
See us hop and jump.

Dora has her doll Jane.
" Jane is my doll. She is
    a big doll," said Dora.

Dora sits by the tree
    to play with her doll.

May will skip.

Dora will bring Fluff's basket.
She will sit the big doll
    in it.

Dora will wash Jane.
She is a big doll,
and Dora can wash her.

Dora has a line by the tree.

May sits on a seat to see
Dora wash the doll.

" Bow-wow, bow-wow,"
said Nip.
" You will not wash me."

Nip runs to the tree.

The doll is on a seat
    by the tree.
She is wet.

Nip can see the doll.
He is a bad dog.
Nip jumps up.

Do you see him ?

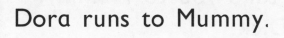

He is on the seat.
The doll is not
    on the seat.
She is in the mud.

Dora runs to Mummy.

Mummy said to Dora,
    " You wash the doll,
    and I will wash Nip."

Jack can not skip well.
He fell and cut his knee.

" Dick, see my knee.
It is cut," he said.

" I will take you to Mummy,"
said Dick.

" Take him to Mummy,"
said Dora.
" She will wash it for him."

Jack hops with Dick
to Mummy.

Mummy will wash his knee
and stick a plaster
on the cut.

It will get well.

The knee has a plaster on it,
so Jack has to hop.

Mummy runs
   with Dick and Dora.

" Stop," said Mummy.
   " You run so fast.
   I can not run so fast.
   I will sit on the seat.
   You can run."

So she sits on the seat.

The cat can see her.
Fluff jumps on the seat
   to sit with Mummy.

" Do you see Mummy ? "
said May.
" I will go to her."

" Bow-wow, bow-wow,
do take me," said Nip.

" No, no," said May.

May runs to Mummy.

" Good-bye, Dora.
Good-bye, Dick," said May.

This is a shop.
You see it is a toy shop.

We will go to the shop
with Mummy.

" Mummy will get us a toy,"
said Dora.

Here are the toys
in the shop.

We can see a small doll
and a big doll.

Here we see a small dog
and a small cat.
The small dog can sit up.
Do you see him ?

Here are the toys,
a small doll and a big doll,
a small cat and a small dog.

One toy can jump.
It is a jumping toy.
It can go, jump, jump,
    jumping on the seat.
Dick has this toy.

He said to Jack,
    " Can you see
    my jumping toy ?
    It can jump well."

Dick and Dora
   are in the shop.

Dick said, "I am big.
   I will get a big bat."

Dora said, "I am big.
   I will get a big ball."

"We will go with the toys
   to Mummy," said Dick.

"No, no, no," said Nip.
   "Do get me a small ball."

"Will you play with me?"
said Dora.

"I will play," said May.
"I will take my doll.
You bring a doll,
so you can play with me.
I will wash the doll
for you."

Jack said to Dick,
  " Will you play with me ? "

Dick said, " I will play.
  I will bring this toy.
  It is my jumping toy.
  It jumps fast."

Fluff said to Nip,
  " Will you play with me
  and the little kitten ? "

Nip said, " I will bring
  this small ball
  for the kitten."

Mummy can see us play.
She sits on the seat
  by the big tree.

Phonic Lists

The attitudes that pupils form towards word-wholes in their early reading experiences are of major importance for all later reading, but at about a *mental* age of 6 years they need the help afforded by phonic practice. But it must be the right kind of practice. It is inadvisable to drill pupils in the tables of an elaborate phonic scheme which includes all phonic units. Such a task is too great and the burden of useless words—words that will not come into their reading vocabulary for several years—is too heavy.

The most practical phonic scheme, after a start has been made through the sentence method, is to base the study of phonic families on words in the actual book being read and in the books to be read in the immediate future. Such phonic practice does not aim at developing a hypothetical phonic ability, but is a direct teaching of units to help pupils to recognise words they are meeting day by day.

The lists of words given here constitute a graded phonic scheme compiled from material in the Introductory Book and Book One, and from common words which provide a direct preparation for Book Two and Book Three of *Happy Venture*.

Groups of common words containing short vowels *a, e, i, o* or *u*.

at	it	get	not	run
cat	bit	let	cot	runs
bat	hit	met	dot	bun
fat	pit	pet	got	fun
hat	sit	net	hot	gun
mat	sits	set	lot	sun
rat		wet	pot	
sat		yet		

Groups of common words containing short vowels *a, e, i, o* or *u*.

big	an	Nip	dog	bad
fig	can	dip	fog	had
pig	man	lip	log	lad
dig	pan	skip		sad
	ran	tip		dad

mud	cap	bed	hop	am
bud	lap	fed	mop	jam
	map	led	pop	ham
	tap	red	top	ram

leg	up	rag	did	cut
beg	cup	bag	hid	but
peg	pup	wag	lid	hut
			kid	nut

Words containing short vowel *a*, *e*, *i*, *o* or *u*, with some common consonant combinations, e.g. *nd*, *st*.

in	hen	dug	ill
bin	den	hug	will
fin	men	jug	bill
pin	pen	mug	fill
tin	ten	rug	hill
win		tug	mill
			pill
			till

fell	six	and	must
bell	fix	hand	dust
sell	mix	band	just
tell		land	rust
well	box	sand	
yell	fox		

Words containing short vowel *a, e, i, o* or *u*, with some common
consonant combinations, e.g. *st, ng, ck*.

best	sing	Dick	back
nest	ring	sick	pack
rest	bring	lick	sack
west	string	pick	tack
		stick	Jack
		chick	

deck	lock	duck	all
neck	rock	luck	ball
peck	sock	suck	call
		tuck	fall
	huff	truck	hall
full	puff		small
pull	Fluff		tall
bull	off		wall

Words containing short vowel *a, e, i, o* or *u*, with some common consonant combinations, e.g. *ch, ck, sh, st, th.*

much	wash	shoe	chick
such	dish	she	chicken
each	fish	shop	chin
rich	wish	shut	chop
march	rush	shall	chap
catch	hush	ship	chimney
match	dash	shed	

stop	rang	thin	this
still	hang	think	then
stick	sang	thank	that
stand		thing	them
story	long	thick	there
stuck	song	third	

Word List

This list contains all the new words used in Book One. There are 60 words in all and the numbers refer to the pages on which the words are first used. There is an average of 2 new words per page, that is, I new word to every 21 words of reading matter. This provides adequate repetition of new words and consolidation of words from the Introductory Book.

Material for revision is provided on page 15 and pages 31-33.

2 basket
for

3 little
kitten
Fluff's

4 stop
her

5 he
on
bad

6 did

7 so
sit
Dick's

shoe
we

8 said

9 wash
off

10 hops
line
my
hop

12 me
one
two

13 jump
do
jumps

14 kittens
up

16 his
bat
throw
hit

18 hits
throws
three

22 seat
bow-wow

23 him

27 go
no
good-bye

19 skip
well
May

24 cut
knee

28 shop
toy

20 us

25 stick
plaster

29 small
are
toys

21 doll

26 fast

30 jumping

Small and Capital Letters

List of letters, small and capital, that the teacher can use for reference with pupils during oral reading if revision of sounds is required.

a	b	c	d	e	f
g	h	i	j	k	l
m	n	o	p	q	r
s	t	u	v	w	x
y	z				

A	B	C	D	E	F
G	H	I	J	K	L
M	N	O	P	Q	R
S	T	U	V	W	X
Y	Z				